WHY THIS IS AN EASY READER

- This story has been carefully written to keep the young reader's interest high.

- It is told in a simple, open style, with a strong rhythm that adds enjoyment both to reading aloud and silent reading.

- There is a very high percentage of words repeated. It is this skillful repetition which helps the child to read independently. Seeing words again and again, he "practices" the vocabulary he knows, and learns with ease the words that are new.

- Only 196 words have been used, with plurals and root words counted once.

   More than one-half of the total vocabulary has been used at least three times.

   Over one-fourth of the total vocabulary has been used at least six times.

   Some words have been used 13, 15, and 30 times.

ABOUT THIS STORY

- This story tells a youngster that other people have the same worries as he: "What will it be like to move?" "How will people like me in a new place?" It can also help him see that changes in life need not be threatening. A good jumping-off point for discussion by children of their own feelings or experiences.

How to Find a Friend

Story by SARA ASHERON
Pictures by SUSAN PERL
Editorial Consultant: LILIAN MOORE

GROSSET & DUNLAP
Publishers
New York, N. Y. 10010

Introduction

These books are meant to help the young reader discover what a delightful experience reading can be. The stories are such fun that they urge the child to try his new reading skills. They are so easy to read that they will encourage and strengthen him as a reader.

The adult will notice that the sentences aren't too long, the words aren't too hard, and the skillful repetition is like a helping hand. What the child will feel is: "This is a good story—and I can read it myself!"

For some children, the best way to meet these stories may be to hear them read aloud at first. Others, who are better prepared to read on their own, may need a little help in the beginning—help that is best given freely. Youngsters who have more experience in reading alone—whether in first or second or third grade—will have the immediate joy of reading "all by myself."

These books have been planned to help all young readers grow—in their pleasure in books and in their power to read them.

Lilian Moore
Specialist in Reading
Formerly of Division of Instructional Research,
New York City Board of Education

"Benny," said his father,
"I have a surprise!"

"A BIG surprise,"
said his mother.

7

"Is it a big cake?"

asked Benny.

His mother laughed.

"No, not a cake,"

she said.

"Is it a big bike
or a big TV?" asked Benny.

"No," said his father.
"It's not that kind of surprise."

"I give up!" said Benny.

"Oh, Benny!" said his mother.

"We are going to MOVE!"

She was so happy,

she gave Benny a big hug.

"We are going to move to a HOUSE—
a house with lots of room,
with a room for you, too!"

11

"The house has a big back yard,"
said Benny's father.
"There's grass in the yard,
and a nice low tree to climb."
Benny's father looked
very happy, too.

13

But Benny was not happy.

"I don't want to move away
from here," he said.

"I don't want to move away
from all my friends."

"But, Benny," said his father,
"there will be children
to play with
on the new street."

"They don't know me," said Benny,
"and I don't know them."

"You will," said his mother.

15

"Oh, Mom!" said Benny.

His mother just did not understand.

She did not understand about

finding new friends.

Benny looked around for his dog.

It was time to take Rex out.

"Here, Rex!" he called.

"Here, boy!"

Benny and Rex ran down the street.

Then they ran all the way back.

They played run-for-the-ball.

They played go-get-the-stick.

Then Boxer came running up to Rex.

Boxer and Rex were old friends.

Boxer wanted to play, too.

But he did not run after the ball

or the stick.

He ran after Rex,

and the dogs had a good time.

Then Benny walked home with Rex.
He sat down outside the house
with his dog.

"You don't want to move away, Rex,
do you?" he asked.

"Woof!" said Rex.

"That's what I thought!"
said Benny.

It was time to go in.

"You don't want to move away
from Boxer, do you, Rex?"
Benny asked.

"Woof, woof!" said Rex.

"That's just what I thought!"
said Benny.
Poor Rex!
He had to move away
from all his friends, too.

Moving day came very soon—

too soon for Benny.

A big moving van pulled up

right outside Benny's house.

Then the moving men
began to take things
out of the house.

In and out they went.

There was his bike.

There was his bed.

There was his box of toys,

and his little chair,

and his books,

all going out of the house
and into the van.

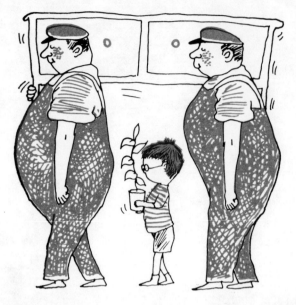

The men let Benny help a little,

and that was fun.

But soon it was time to go

to the new house—

and that was no fun, at all!

Oh, the new house WAS pretty.

The yard WAS big.

There WAS grass.

And, yes, there WAS

a nice low tree to climb.

But Benny was not happy.

He looked up and down the street.

"I don't see anyone to play with,"

he thought.

"Maybe I will never have
a friend here," he thought.
"Maybe I will never have
anyone to play with but Rex."
Then he called,
"Here, Rex!
Here, boy!"

Rex did not come running.

Benny called again,

"Here, Rex!

Here, boy!"

But Rex did not come.

Benny ran into the house.

"Mom," he said, "did you see Rex?"

"Yes," said his mother.

"I saw him go down the street.

I thought he was with you."

The boy came across the street
to Benny.

"Did your dog run away?"
he asked.

"No," said Benny.

"We just moved here,
and Rex may not know
the way home."

"My name is Nick," said the boy.

"Do you want me to help you

look for him?"

"Thanks! said Benny.

"Thanks a lot!"

"Let's look down this next street,"
said Nick.

"Dogs like to dig there."

They walked to the next street.

Benny saw a boy and a girl
across the street.
But no Rex.

"Hi, Billy!" Nick called.

"Hi, Jenny!

This is Benny.

He can't find his dog."

The boy and girl

ran across the street to Benny.

"We can help you look for him,"

said Jenny.

"Let's try the meat store,"

said Billy.

"Dogs like to go there."

They all went to the meat store.

But Rex was not there.

"Maybe he went this way,"
said Nick.
"Dogs like to play
in the grass over there."
So they all went on
to the next street.
Benny saw a girl
across the street.
But no Rex.

"Hi, Betsy!"

Jenny called to the girl.

"This is Benny.

He can't find his dog."

The girl ran across the street.

"I can help you look for him,"

she said.

They all walked down
the next street.
Benny was looking
and looking for Rex,
so he did not know
that they had walked
all around the block.
All at once, he stopped in surprise.
"Say, that's my house!" he cried.

"Is THAT your house?" asked Nick.
"I live right across the street —
over there!"

"And we live over there!"
said Billy.

"In that house with the white door,"
said Jenny.

"And I live over there!"
said Betsy.
"In that house right by
the big tree."

Benny was so surprised that
he forgot about Rex.
He looked at Nick,

and Billy,

and Jenny,

and Betsy.

"Say," he cried,

"there's a good tree for climbing

in my back yard.

Want to try it?"

They all ran into the back yard.

Benny stopped.

"Look!" he said.

And he began to laugh.

There was Rex—happy as anything!

There he was, playing with two dogs!

"Well, look at that!"

said Nick.

He began to laugh, too.

"Your dog has found

some new friends!"

Benny looked at Rex.

Then he looked at the children.

"So have I!"

he thought in surprise.

Then he said, "Come on!"

And they all ran over

to climb on the nice low tree.